Tiger Team 4
My Progress Journal

My Language Passport	page	2
1 A New School Year	page	3
2 Describing People	page	6
3 Around the Town	page	9
4 Jobs and Routines	page	12
5 Things We Like Doing	page	15
6 In the Countryside	page	18
7 Tiger Street Club Review	page	21

Carol Read • Mark Ormerod

My Language Passport

Stick your photo here.

My name is _____
_____.
I'm _____ years old.
My birthday is in _____.
I live in _____.

My school
My school is called _____
_____.
This year, I'm in class _____.

My languages
I speak _____.
I'm learning to speak _____.

My English lessons
I've got English on ☐ Mondays   ☐ Tuesdays   ☐ Wednesdays
                     ☐ Thursdays ☐ Fridays   ☐ Saturdays

My English teacher is called _____.

1 A New School Year

My learning review

1 Do you remember the story? Tell a friend or your family. Use some of these words to help you.

back at school   music book
recorder   Oliver
terrible noise   after school
teach Ellie to play   member

2 What has your school got? Write sentences.

My school has got _____

_____

_____.

My school hasn't got _____

_____

_____.

My vocabulary check

3 Do you remember the key words from Unit 1? Write them in the columns.

My five favourite subjects	Other subjects
_____	_____
_____	_____
_____	_____
_____	_____
_____	_____

My learning

4. Think about your favourite activity in Unit 1. How does it help you to learn? Write and circle.

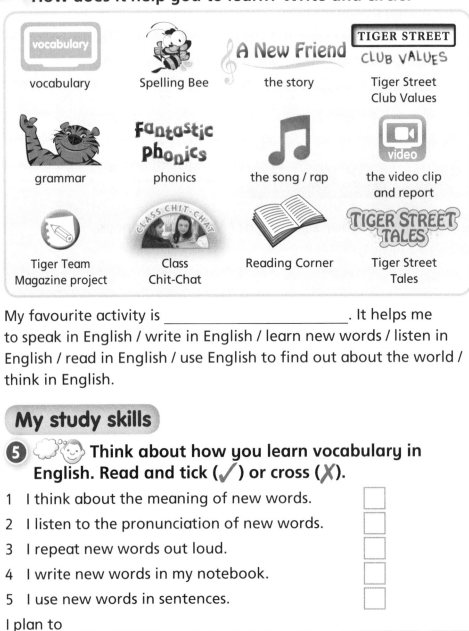

vocabulary   Spelling Bee   the story   Tiger Street Club Values

grammar   phonics   the song / rap   the video clip and report

Tiger Team Magazine project   Class Chit-Chat   Reading Corner   Tiger Street Tales

My favourite activity is _____. It helps me to speak in English / write in English / learn new words / listen in English / read in English / use English to find out about the world / think in English.

My study skills

5. Think about how you learn vocabulary in English. Read and tick (✓) or cross (✗).

1. I think about the meaning of new words.
2. I listen to the pronunciation of new words.
3. I repeat new words out loud.
4. I write new words in my notebook.
5. I use new words in sentences.

I plan to _____.

My progress

6 What can you do after Unit 1?
Read and circle your score.

1 = I can't do this very well.   5 = I can do this easily and well.

1	I can name school subjects.	1 2 3 4 5
2	I can ask about and talk about my school timetable.	1 2 3 4 5
3	I can act out the *A New Friend* story.	1 2 3 4 5
4	I can sing the *What have we got?* song.	1 2 3 4 5
5	I know about different types of schools.	1 2 3 4 5
6	I can write about my school.	1 2 3 4 5

My score for Unit 1:   / 30

My learning plan

7 How do you plan to remember Unit 1? Write.

- read Unit 1 again
- write a list of words to remember
- learn the grammar table
- do the online activities

I plan to _____

_____

_____

_____ .

2 Describing People

My learning review

1 Do you remember the story? Write sentences about the character.

He's got _____ _____ _____ _____ _____.

He hasn't got _____ _____ _____ _____ _____.

2 What is your favourite book? Make notes.

- Title: _____
- Author: _____
- Type of book: _____
- Description of my favourite character: _____
  _____

My vocabulary check

3 Do you remember the key words from Unit 2? Look, order and write the words.

raif raih
fair hair

chatmouse
_____

grattish arih
_____

lurcy hira
_____

trosh rhia
_____

glon arih
_____

krad airh
_____

dreab
_____

pontyali
_____

slagses
_____

My learning

4 Think about your favourite activity in Unit 2. How does it help you to learn? Write and circle.

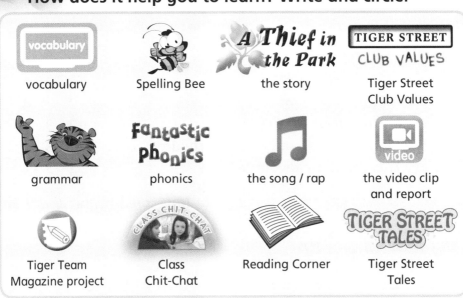

My favourite activity is _____. It helps me to speak in English / write in English / learn new words / listen in English / read in English / use English to find out about the world / think in English.

My study skills

5 Think about how you read in English. Read and tick (✓) or cross (✗).

1 I read something in English every week.
2 I read and listen to texts at the same time.
3 I read and sing the songs in *Pop Spot*.
4 I read out loud on my own.
5 I read interesting texts more than once.

I plan to _____.

My progress

6 What can you do after Unit 2?
Read and circle your score.

1 = I can't do this very well.   5 = I can do this easily and well.

1 I can name different types of hair.	1 2 3 4 5
2 I can describe people.	1 2 3 4 5
3 I can act out the *A Thief in the Park* story.	1 2 3 4 5
4 I can sing the *Stop! Thief!* song.	1 2 3 4 5
5 I know about four great books for children.	1 2 3 4 5
6 I can write about my favourite book.	1 2 3 4 5

My score for Unit 2:   / 30

My learning plan

7 How do you plan to remember Unit 2? Write.

- read Unit 2 again
- write a list of words to remember
- learn the grammar table
- do the online activities

I plan to _____

_____

_____

_____.

3 Around the Town

My learning review

1 Do you remember the story? Write sentences.

follow   flute   ~~shops~~   money

1 In Hamlin, <u>there are shops and people and rats.</u>
2 The piper _____.
3 The rats _____.
4 The mayor _____.

2 What types of transport do people use? Look and complete the sentences.

In London, people travel by taxi, _____ and _____.

In Venice, people travel by _____ and water bus.

In Amsterdam, people travel by tram and _____.

Where I live, people travel by _____.

My vocabulary check

3 Do you remember the key words from Unit 3? Use some of them to complete the sentences.

In my town, there's a _____.

In my town, there are _____.

My learning

④ Think about your favourite activity in Unit 3. How does it help you to learn? Write and circle.

My favourite activity is _____. It helps me to speak in English / write in English / learn new words / listen in English / read in English / use English to find out about the world / think in English.

My study skills

⑤ Think about how you practise pronunciation in English. Read and tick (✓) or cross (✗).

1 I imitate my teacher and the CD.
2 I read and listen to the sentences in *Fantastic Phonics*.
3 I memorise and repeat the sentences in *Fantastic Phonics*.
4 I act out dialogues in class.
5 I read and sing songs in English.

I plan to _____.

My progress

6 What can you do after Unit 3?
Read and circle your score.

1 = I can't do this very well.   5 = I can do this easily and well.

1	I can name places in towns and cities.	1 2 3 4 5
2	I can ask about and say what there is in my street.	1 2 3 4 5
3	I can act out *The Piper of Hamlin* story.	1 2 3 4 5
4	I can sing the *Near here* song.	1 2 3 4 5
5	I know about types of transport in cities.	1 2 3 4 5
6	I can write about where I live.	1 2 3 4 5

My score for Unit 3:   / 30

My learning plan

7 How do you plan to remember Unit 3? Write.

- read Unit 3 again
- write a list of words to remember
- learn the grammar table
- do the online activities

I plan to _____

_____

_____

_____ .

4 Jobs and Routines

My learning review

1 Do you remember the story? Write four more questions the children ask about Lulu.

1 Does she design clothes?
2 _____
3 _____
4 _____
5 _____

2 What do working dogs do? Write sentences.

1 Josh is a mountain rescue dog. He uses his nose to find people lost in the mountains.
2 Milton is _____ . _____
3 Lady is _____ . _____

My vocabulary check

3 Do you remember the key words from Unit 4? Write them in alphabetical order.

1 farmer   6 _____
2 _____   7 _____
3 _____   8 _____
4 _____   9 _____
5 _____   10 _____

My learning

4 Think about your favourite activity in Unit 4. How does it help you to learn? Write and circle.

My favourite activity is _____. It helps me to speak in English / write in English / learn new words / listen in English / read in English / use English to find out about the world / think in English.

My study skills

5 Think about how you write in English. Read and tick (✓) or cross (✗).

1 I think about what I want to write.
2 I make a plan.
3 I write neatly.
4 I use a dictionary.
5 I learn from my mistakes.

I plan to _____.

My progress

6 What can you do after Unit 4?
Read and circle your score.

1 = I can't do this very well.   5 = I can do this easily and well.

1	I can name jobs.	1 2 3 4 5
2	I can ask about and say what people do.	1 2 3 4 5
3	I can act out the *A Visitor at School* story.	1 2 3 4 5
4	I can sing the *What's his job?* song.	1 2 3 4 5
5	I can name three types of working dogs.	1 2 3 4 5
6	I can write about someone who works in my community.	1 2 3 4 5

My score for Unit 4:   / 30

My learning plan

7 How do you plan to remember Unit 4? Write.

- read Unit 4 again
- write a list of words to remember
- learn the grammar table
- do the online activities

I plan to _____

_____

_____

_____ .

5 Things We Like Doing

My learning review

1 Do you remember the story? Tell a friend or your family. Use these pictures to help you.

2 What can you see in galleries and museums? Write.

> drawings   artists   inventors   inventions   sculptures   paintings

1 In science museums, you can find out about the lives of scientists and _____. You can see great _____.
2 In art galleries, you can find out about the lives of _____. You can see their _____, _____ and _____.

My vocabulary check

3 Do you remember the key words from Unit 5? Write them in the columns.

Activities I like doing	Activities I don't like doing
_____	_____
_____	_____
_____	_____
_____	_____

My learning

4 🗨️ Think about your favourite activity in Unit 5. How does it help you to learn? Write and circle.

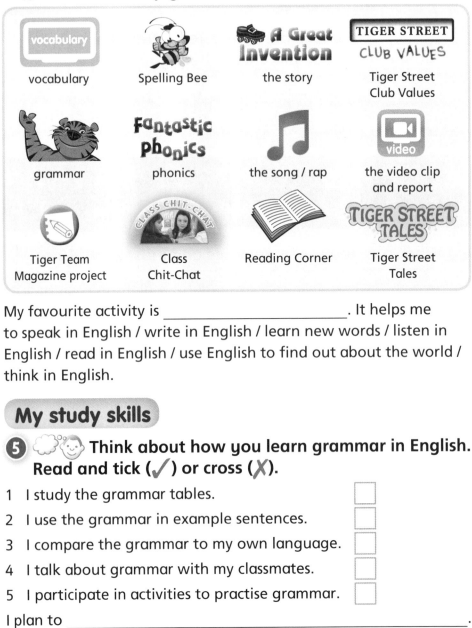

vocabulary	Spelling Bee	the story	Tiger Street Club Values
grammar	phonics	the song / rap	the video clip and report
Tiger Team Magazine project	Class Chit-Chat	Reading Corner	Tiger Street Tales

My favourite activity is _____. It helps me to speak in English / write in English / learn new words / listen in English / read in English / use English to find out about the world / think in English.

My study skills

5 🗨️ Think about how you learn grammar in English. Read and tick (✓) or cross (✗).

1 I study the grammar tables. ☐
2 I use the grammar in example sentences. ☐
3 I compare the grammar to my own language. ☐
4 I talk about grammar with my classmates. ☐
5 I participate in activities to practise grammar. ☐

I plan to _____.

My progress

6 What can you do after Unit 5?
Read and circle your score.

1 = I can't do this very well.   5 = I can do this easily and well.

1	I can name activities I like.	1 2 3 4 5
2	I can ask about and say what I like doing.	1 2 3 4 5
3	I can act out the *A Great Invention* story.	1 2 3 4 5
4	I can sing the *What do you like doing?* song.	1 2 3 4 5
5	I know about what you can see in galleries and museums.	1 2 3 4 5
6	I can write about what I like doing at the weekends.	1 2 3 4 5

My score for Unit 5:   / 30

My learning plan

7 How do you plan to remember Unit 5? Write.

- read Unit 5 again
- write a list of words to remember
- learn the grammar table
- do the online activities

I plan to _____

_____

_____

_____ .

6 In the Countryside

My learning review

1 Do you remember the story? Tell a friend or your family. Use some of these words to help you.

campsite   forest   list   take photos
ghost orchid   badger   broken leg
rescue services   newspaper

2 What animals and plants live in or grow on trees? Draw and write the words.

mushrooms

My vocabulary check

3 Do you remember the key words from Unit 6? Look and write.

river

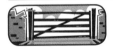   

18

My learning

4. Think about your favourite activity in Unit 6. How does it help you to learn? Write and circle.

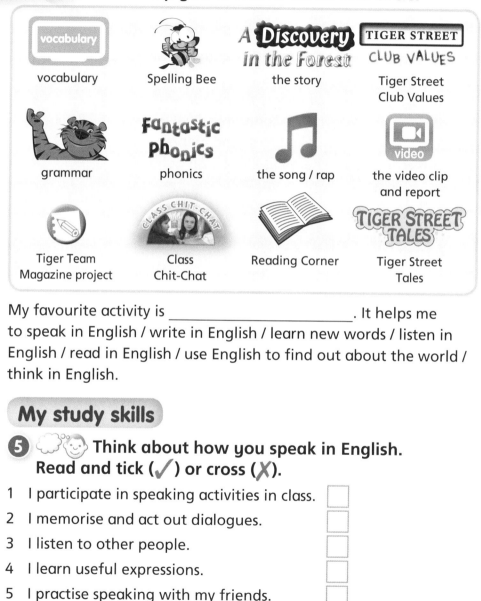

My favourite activity is _____. It helps me to speak in English / write in English / learn new words / listen in English / read in English / use English to find out about the world / think in English.

My study skills

5. Think about how you speak in English. Read and tick (✓) or cross (✗).

1 I participate in speaking activities in class. ☐
2 I memorise and act out dialogues. ☐
3 I listen to other people. ☐
4 I learn useful expressions. ☐
5 I practise speaking with my friends. ☐

I plan to _____.

My progress

6 What can you do after Unit 6?
Read and circle your score.

1 = I can't do this very well.   5 = I can do this easily and well.

1	I can name things you see in the countryside.	1 2 3 4 5
2	I can ask and give directions.	1 2 3 4 5
3	I can act out the *A Discovery in the Forest* story.	1 2 3 4 5
4	I can sing *The way to the campsite* song.	1 2 3 4 5
5	I know about arboreal animals and plants.	1 2 3 4 5
6	I can write about where I like to go on holiday.	1 2 3 4 5

My score for Unit 6:   / 30

My learning plan

7 How do you plan to remember Unit 6? Write.

- read Unit 6 again
- write a list of words to remember
- learn the grammar table
- do the online activities

I plan to _____

_____

_____

_____ .

_____

7 Tiger Street Club Review

My learning review

1 Match the scene titles to the words. Use the words to tell the story to a friend or your family.

The flying machine The journey Coming home Phileas is famous

| fly Venice London | Phileas digital camera eighty minutes | newspapers television really cool | on fire caretaker fire brigade |

2 Who works on the films you watch at the cinema? Write definitions.

The writer _writes the screenplay_.
The director _____.
The cameraman _____.
The actors _____.
The make-up artist _____.

My vocabulary check

3 Do you remember the key words from Unit 7? Write them in the columns.

Things in movies People in movies
clapperboard

My learning

4 Think about your favourite activity in Unit 7. How does it help you to learn? Write and circle.

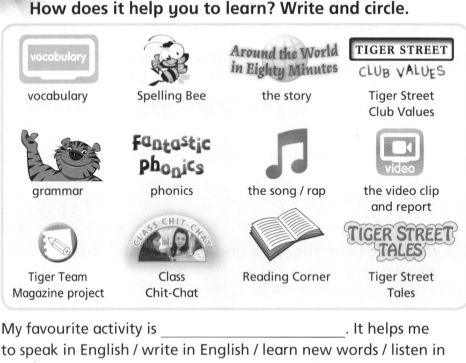

My favourite activity is _____. It helps me to speak in English / write in English / learn new words / listen in English / read in English / use English to find out about the world / think in English.

My study skills

5 Think about how you practise English. Read and tick (✓) or cross (✗).

1 I watch TV and films in English.
2 I listen to English pop songs.
3 I send emails and text messages in English.
4 I read magazines and books in English.
5 I talk to my friends in English.

I plan to _____.

My progress

6 What can you do after Unit 7?
Read and circle your score.

1 = I can't do this very well.   5 = I can do this easily and well.

1	I can name things related to making movies.	1 2 3 4 5
2	I can use language and vocabulary in *Tiger Team 4*.	1 2 3 4 5
3	I can act out the *Around the World in Eighty Minutes* screenplay.	1 2 3 4 5
4	I can sing the *Let's make a movie* song.	1 2 3 4 5
5	I know about people who work making movies.	1 2 3 4 5
6	I can write a report about my progress in English.	1 2 3 4 5

My score for Unit 7:   / 30

My learning plan

7 How do you plan to remember Unit 7? Write.

- read Unit 7 again
- write a list of words to remember
- look at all my work in *Tiger Team 4*
- practise English in the holidays

I plan to _____

_____

_____

_____.

Macmillan Education
4 Crinan Street
London N1 9XW
A division of Macmillan Publishers Limited
Companies and representatives throughout the world

ISBN 978 0 230 43114 0

Text © Carol Read and Mark Ormerod 2013
Design and illustration © Macmillan Publishers Limited 2013

First published 2013

All rights reserved; no part of this publication may be reproduced, stored in a retrieval system, transmitted in any form, or by any means, electronic, mechanical, photocopying, recording, or otherwise, without the prior written permission of the publishers.

Designed by Carolyn Gibson
Illustrated by Lisa Althaus, Kevin Hopgood, Graham Howells, Martin Impey, Andrew Painter, Pete Smith and Simon Walmesley
Cover design by Astwood Design Consultancy
Cover photographs by Macmillan Publishers Ltd / Stuart Cox

The authors and publishers would like to thank the following for permission to reproduce their photographs: Macmillan Publishers Ltd/Stuart Cox p3; Rex Features p12 (1, 2, 3); Superstock/Radius pp 4, 7, 10, 13, 16, 19, 22

Printed and bound in China

2018 2017 2016
10 9 8